Wildflowers
to Color

Illustrated by Jenny Cooper

Designed by Nelupa Hussain
Written by Susan Meredith

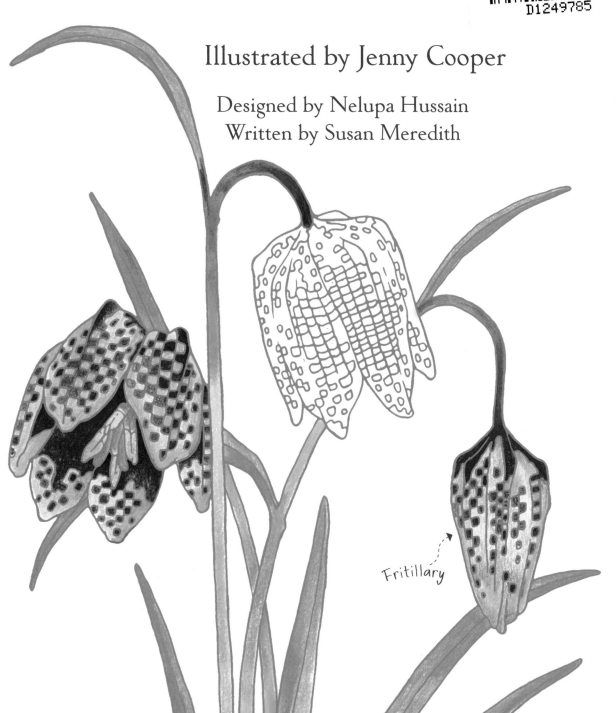

Fritillary

Coneflowers

Coneflowers are a type of daisy. They're big and bright, and grow in eastern and central North America.

Their scientific name is echinacea (pronounced ekin-ay-sha), which comes from the Greek for 'hedgehog'.

The flowers have a prickly, cone-shaped center.

When the flowers are fully open, the petals tend to point downwards.

This is called a purple coneflower, although it looks more pink than purple.

Yellow coneflower

The leaves are rough and hairy.

Some people think that taking echinacea remedies – made from purple coneflowers – prevents colds.

Scarlet pimpernels

Scarlet pimpernels grow almost all over the world. The flowers are often more salmon-colored than scarlet, and some are blue.

They have five petals ...

... and oval-shaped leaves.

Five vivid yellow stamens hold pollen.

Bud

The flowers grow on long, straggly stalks.

Scarlet pimpernels are also known as 'shepherd's barometer' because they open when it's sunny and close when it's dull.

Shooting stars

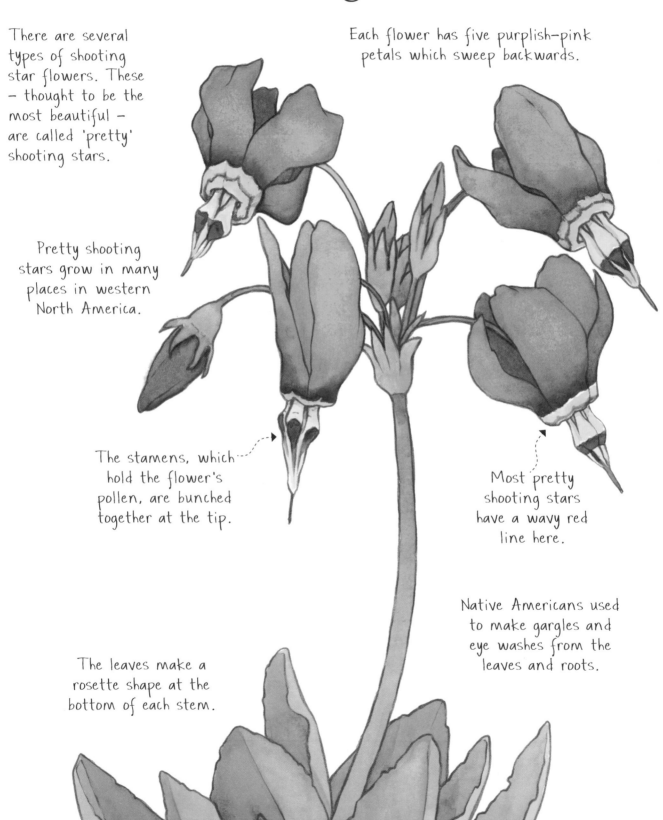

There are several types of shooting star flowers. These — thought to be the most beautiful — are called 'pretty' shooting stars.

Each flower has five purplish-pink petals which sweep backwards.

Pretty shooting stars grow in many places in western North America.

The stamens, which hold the flower's pollen, are bunched together at the tip.

Most pretty shooting stars have a wavy red line here.

Native Americans used to make gargles and eye washes from the leaves and roots.

The leaves make a rosette shape at the bottom of each stem.

Morning glory

There are hundreds of types of morning glories. This one, known as 'dwarf' morning glory, grows in the dry, sunny climates of southern Europe and North Africa.

Each flower comes into bloom one morning, then curls up and dies later the same day. But the plant keeps on producing new flowers all season.

The flowers have a yellow 'throat'.

In northern Europe, wild morning glory is pink or white, not blue.

Striped bud

Some types of morning glories are also known as 'bindweed' because they coil themselves around things.

Cowslips

Cowslips are found mainly in northern and central Europe. The name cowslip comes from an old English word for cow dung — the flowers often appear among cow pies in fields.

The tube-shaped flowers grow in clusters, usually drooping to one side of the stem. They have a sweet scent.

Each petal has an orange blob at its base.

Duke of Burgundy butterflies lay their eggs on cowslip leaves and their caterpillars eat them.

The wrinkled, tongue-shaped leaves form a rosette at the base of the stems.

Asters

Asters grow wild mainly in North America. They belong to the daisy family and are also known as 'Michaelmas daisies'.

They grow in tall clumps, with the brilliant flowers appearing in late summer and early fall.

Monarch butterfly

Butterflies and bees like asters. They visit them to drink the sweet, sugary nectar in the flowers.

These are New England asters, named after the area of North America where they're found. Some other types of asters have pink flowers instead of purple.

Bud

Long, pointed leaves

Poppies, cornflowers and oxeye daisies

These flowers all grow in fields of corn and other grain.

Poppies have dazzling red, silky petals that dance in the breeze.

These pods hold a poppy's seeds — more than a thousand in each one.

Some poppies have black blotches at the base of their petals.

Poppy buds hang down.

Oxeye daisies are also known as 'moon daisies' because of their yellow centers.

Cornflowers have vivid blue flowers that are purplish in the middle.

They are about ten times bigger than daisies that grow on lawns.

Hairy poppy stem

Butterfly weed

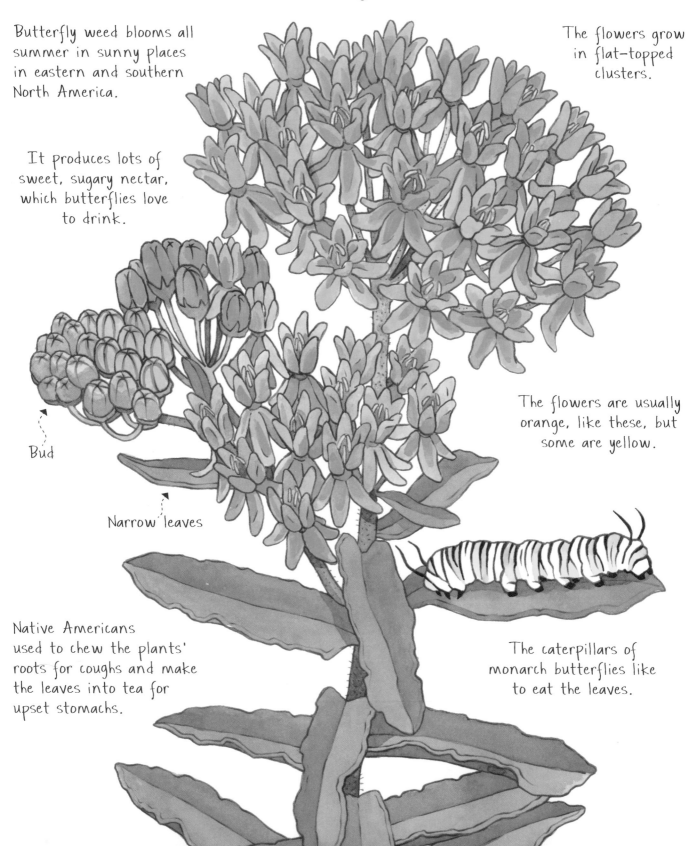

Butterfly weed blooms all summer in sunny places in eastern and southern North America.

It produces lots of sweet, sugary nectar, which butterflies love to drink.

The flowers grow in flat-topped clusters.

The flowers are usually orange, like these, but some are yellow.

Bud

Narrow leaves

Native Americans used to chew the plants' roots for coughs and make the leaves into tea for upset stomachs.

The caterpillars of monarch butterflies like to eat the leaves.

Cranesbills and rock roses

This flowering bush is called 'bloody' cranesbill, because its leaves turn rusty red in fall.

The flowers start off bright pink but turn purplish as they age.

The leaves are split into thin leaflets.

Five delicate, crinkly petals

Wild rock roses, like these, are always yellow. Despite their name, they aren't roses.

The drooping buds have reddish stripes.

The leaves stay on the bush all year.

Bloody cranesbills and rock roses both grow in Europe, often among rocks.

Viper's bugloss

Viper's bugloss, also known as 'blueweed', grows in Europe, North America and parts of Asia, in bare, dry places. People used to think it cured snake bites.

The trumpet-shaped flowers are brilliant violet-blue ...

... but the buds are pink. They appear from curved green shoots growing off the main stem.

Bumblebee

Bees, butterflies and moths all love to drink the nectar in the flowers.

Large skipper butterfly

Reddish-pink stamens hold the flower's pollen.

The stems have sharp hairs.

Fritillaries

There are over a hundred types of fritillaries. This one is called snake's head fritillary because the nodding buds look a little like snakes' heads.

The flowers' unusual checkered pattern gives them other names too — 'checkered lilies' or 'chess flowers'.

There is usually only one flower on each slender stem.

Many fritillaries have an unpleasant smell and the bulbs they grow from are poisonous.

Bud

Long, thin, pointed leaves

Yellow stamens hold the flower's pollen.

Some snake's head fritillaries are white but they still have a faint checkered pattern.

Indian blankets

Native Americans used to make blankets in combinations of yellow, orange and red, which is how these flowers get their name. They're also known as 'firewheels' or 'sundance flowers'.

The big, bold, daisy-like flowers are common in hot sunny places all across central North America.

Bud

The petals are often split into three prongs at the tips.

Half-open bud

People used to make tea from the plants' roots and drink it for upset stomachs.

Bee orchids

There are over 20,000 types of wild orchids in the world. These bee orchids grow mainly in Europe, especially in the Mediterranean area.

The stems grow tall and straight, with unopened buds at the top.

They get their name because they look like bees resting on pink flowers.

The leaves are long and pointed.

This part is furry, like a bee.

The 'eyes' of the bee

These parts look a little like a bee's antennae.

The 'bee' is actually a part of the flower called the 'lip'. Real bees and other insects perch on it to drink the flower's sweet, sugary nectar.

The 'folded legs' of the bee

Lungworts

Lungworts grow in Europe and western Asia, usually in shady places such as woodlands.

The flowers are reddish-pink when they first open, then gradually change to bluish-purple.

Hairy-footed flower bees like lungworts. They have very long tongues which can reach right into the flowers to drink their sugary nectar.

Spotted leaves

The flowers got their name because people used to think the leaves looked like diseased lungs – and could be used to cure lung infections.

Flame lilies

Flame lilies grow wild in Africa and parts of Asia. Their bright red petals, with wavy yellow edges, look like flames.

The buds droop down ...

... but the petals of the open flowers arch backwards.

The stamens, which hold the flowers' pollen, stick right out below the petals.

Flame lilies climb up other plants. They cling to them with the curly tendrils at the tips of their glossy leaves.

Flame lilies are so prized in Zimbabwe that they've become the country's national flower.

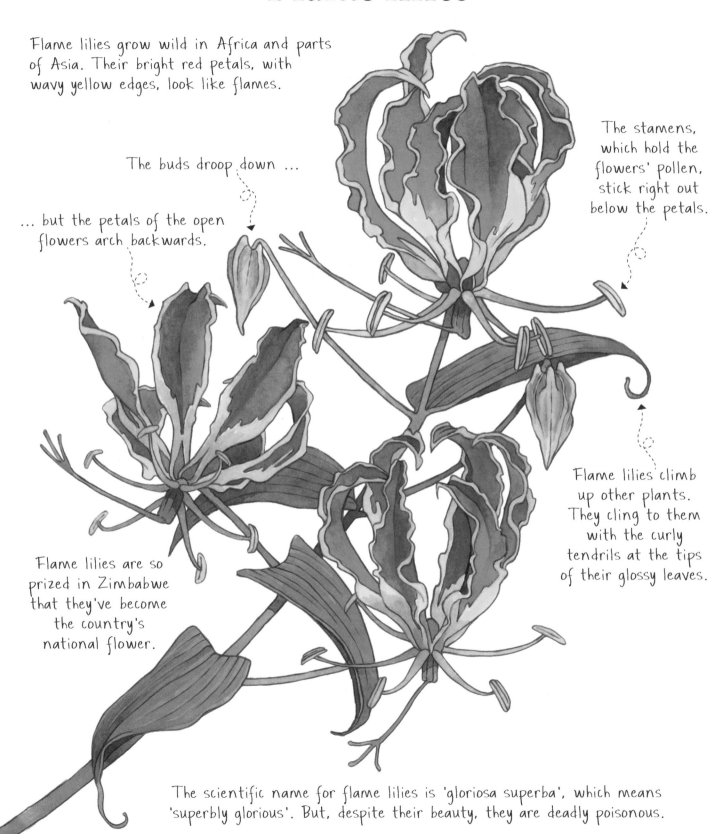

The scientific name for flame lilies is 'gloriosa superba', which means 'superbly glorious'. But, despite their beauty, they are deadly poisonous.

Coloring hints and tips

You can use colored pencils, markers, or watercolor paints or pencils to color in your pictures. If you use watercolors, put a piece of cardboard under your page to keep the rest of the book dry.

Colored pencils

Colored pencils give a soft effect and are good for doing shading.

To fill in large areas, do lots of lines all going in the same direction.

In areas with shading, press firmly for the dark areas, then gradually reduce the pressure where the color gets lighter.

You can blend different colors together by shading them on top of each other.

Watercolors

Make watercolors lighter by adding more water, or darker by adding less.

For distinct colors, let one color dry before you add the next.

Wet watercolors blur together.

Markers

For a bolder effect, without much shading, you could use markers.

Use a fine-tipped pen for small or detailed areas.

With thanks to James Armitage.
Digital manipulation by Nick Wakeford. Americanization by Carrie Armstrong.
First published in 2014 by Usborne Publishing Ltd, Usborne House, 83-85 Saffron Hill, London EC1N 8RT, England. www.usborne.com